What Do You See?
Finding Shapes From The Sky

by
Margot Cheel

To Katherine + Erin,
   Have fun finding shapes!
            Margot Cheel

For my grandchildren
and the curiosity in all of us!

Copyright © 2016 by Margot Cheel

ALL RIGHTS RESERVED.

ISBN 978-0-9852486-2-8

Published by Under the Sky Press
Cohasset, MA 02025

Book design by Ken Burg

Printed in the United States of America
by J. S. McCarthy Printers Hartford, Ct.

FSC MIX
Paper from responsible sources
FSC® C021556
www.fsc.org

2

What Do You See?

This is a book for all ages. Children and Adults.
Come fly above the earth and look down for surprises.
How many shapes, colors and forms can you see?

There are no right or wrong answers,
yet many ways to see these real places on the earth.
Have fun exploring!

3

Have you ever
looked up
at clouds in the sky?

And seen a figure?
A man's face or
something else?

5

What if we went up into the sky in an airplane
and looked down at the earth.
Would we find shapes down below?

What does the big shape look like?
What else do you see?

6

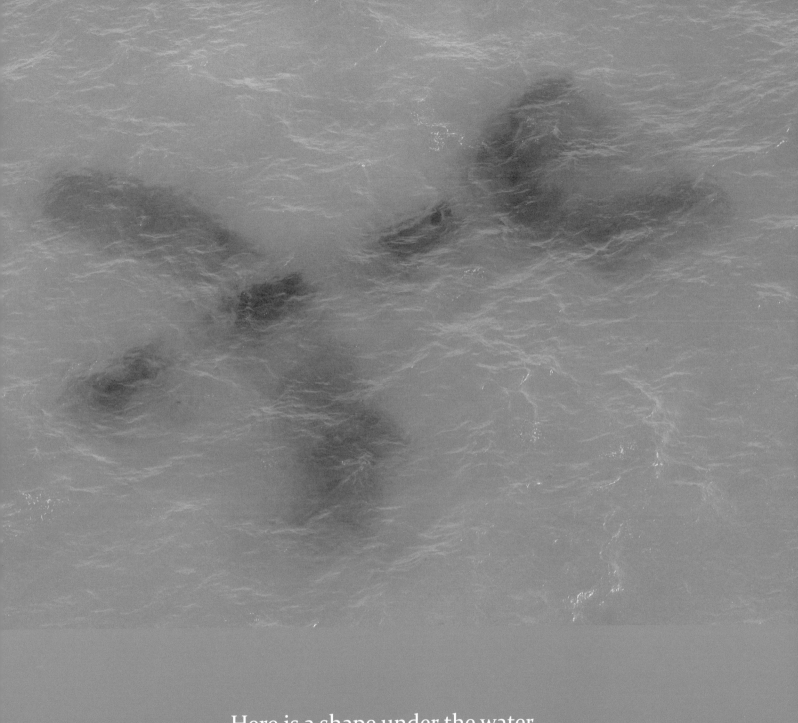

Here is a shape under the water.
What does it look like to you?

7

If you find sand under water, what do you see?

There are lots of lines here.
Do you see shapes in the water and grasses?

There are some rocks by the shore.
Do they look like an animal?

What kind?

10

Wow, from high above you can see things differently.

What is the shape in this field?

Kids and parents made these designs on the ground.

Can you tell from the air what they used to make them?

A shape on the ground can look like something else from high above.
What do you see here?

14

Can you find a little girl below?
What other shapes are near her?

15

16

The sand has made a figure!
What could this be?

Sometimes things can look ...

... spooky down below!

Here is the ocean, but is that a blue ghost?
And other creatures?

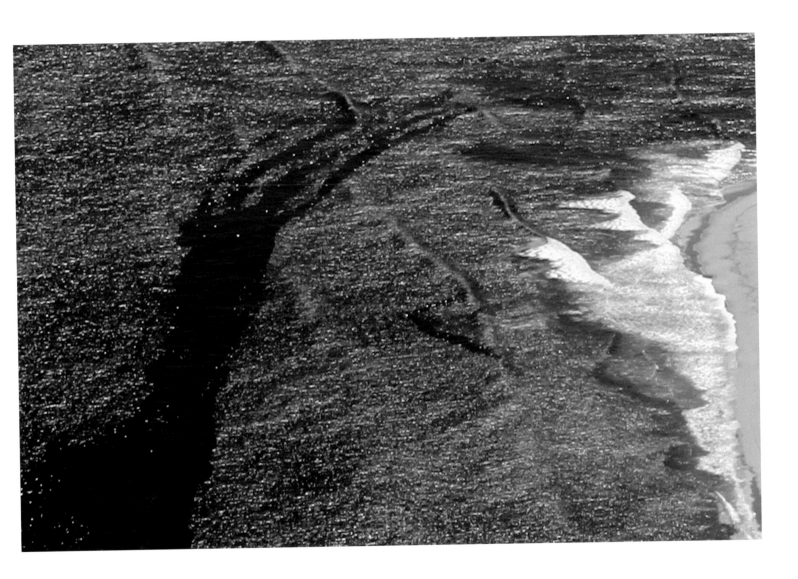

What do you see under the water?

21

22

The beach and ocean
make shapes together.
Do you see faces,
like we did in the clouds?

23

Flying closer,
what do you spot below?
Can you find fish shapes?

24

What can you see here?

It is almost time to fly home and come down from the sky.
But wait, there is something red and black!
What could be red?

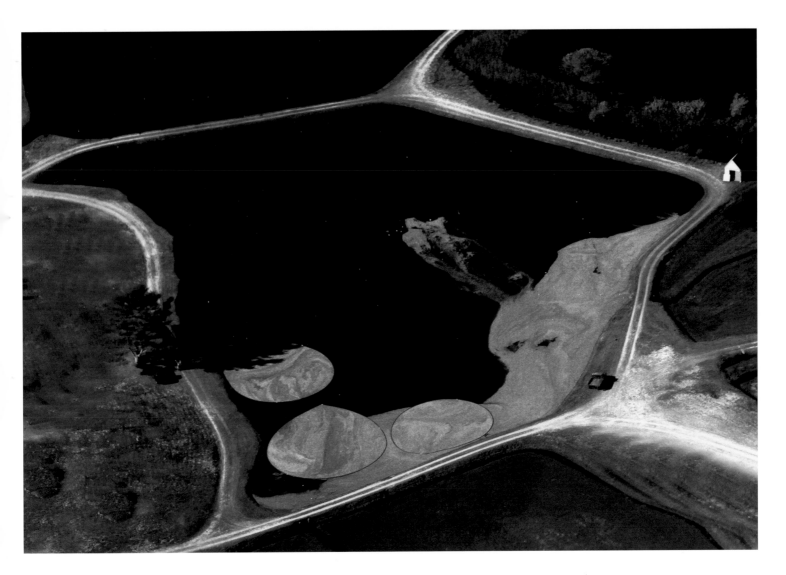

How many shapes can you find?

Remember,
if you fly in an airplane,
or even in your imagination,
you can always see something new each time.

28

All these sights and shapes we have seen from above are real places on the earth. You can discover where - *right here!*

Cover
Cape Cod
Chatham, Ma

Page 7
Key West, FL

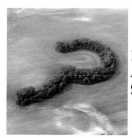

Page 11
A Farm Field,
South Dakota

Page 2
Elizabeth Islands,
Gosnold, MA

Page 8
Nantucket, MA

Page 12
Pumpkin Patch,
Cohasset, MA

Page 3
Elizabeth Islands,
Gosnold, MA

Page 9
Marshfield, MA

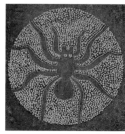

Page 13
Pumpkin Patch,
Cohasset, MA

Page 6
Sakonnet, RI

Page 10
Cohasset, MA

Page 14
Hatherly Golf
Course,
Scituate, MA

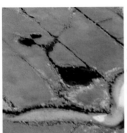 Page 15
Cape Cod
Falmouth, MA

 Pages 20 & 21
Sandy Cove,
Cohasset, MA

 Page 25
Cape Cod
Orleans, MA

 Pages 16 & 17
Cape Cod
Chatham, MA

 Page 22
Humarock, MA

 Page 26
North River
Scituate, MA

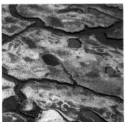 Page 18
South River,
Marshfield, MA

 Page 23
Cape Cod
National Seashore

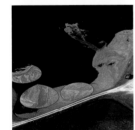 Page 27
Cranberry Bog,
Plymouth, MA

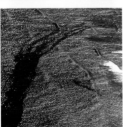 Page 19
Cape Cod
Chatham, MA

 Page 24
Marshfield, MA

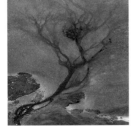 Pages 28 & 29
Duxbury, MA

Margot Cheel is a photographer, pilot, and author. She is an arts graduate of Middlebury College, Vt, an alumnae of WGBH-TV, Boston, co-founder of Twin Willows Craft Center, Ontario, Canada and an arts workshop facilitator.

In her first published book, *"Sea and Sand from the Sky: Aerial Photography"* she found that children spotted figures and forms in the landscape photos. The discovery was always with delight and often to the surprise of parents & adults. Hence this book, *"What Do You See? Finding Shapes from the Sky"* was born.

Purpose

"My goal for this picture book is to tap the creative imagination of child and adult, to encourage a connection to nature and to go beyond a quick glance to further see a place in depth and variation. Here it is with a perspective from above. There is always more than one way of seeing something....and having an adventure in the process!"

Acknowledgements

I am very grateful for assistance from many sources:
The Ninety-Nines – International Organization of Women Pilots for continued inspiration and support; Ken Burg for his technical and creative skills in book design; J.S. McCarthy Printers for their printing services; Many clients and friends who have promoted and supported my art through the years, and my oldest grandchild, Clinton (born 11/23/11) whose exuberance in finding shapes in the photos told me that seeing anew is exciting at any age.

Photos Prints from this book can be ordered at:
www.margotcheel.com
Cohasset, MA